CONTENTS

CHAPTER 1

Nouns	2
Verbs	4
Adjectives	6
Opposites (Antonyms)	8
More Than One (Plurals)	10
The Animal Kingdom	12
Baby Animals	14

CHAPTER 2

Past and Present	16
Double Letters	18
Alphabetical Order	20
Similar Words (Synonyms)	22
Sounds the Same (Homophones)	24
Around the House	26
Parts of the Body	28
Time	30

CHAPTER 3

CrossWord Practice 1	32
CrossWord Practice 2	34
CrossWord Practice 3	36
CrossWord Practice 4	38
CrossWord Practice 5	40
CrossWord Practice 6	42
CrossWord Practice 7	44
CrossWord Practice 8	46
CrossWord Practice 9	48

ANSWERS & STICKERS	50

NOUNS

A NOUN is a NAME. **It can be the name of a person, animal, place or object.**

For example: **Jane** sat on a **chair.**

"Jane" is a noun as it is the name of the **person**.
"Chair" is a noun as it is the name of an **object**.

Below each picture clue are jumbled letters. If you rearrange the letters it will help you find the NOUN. Copy the whole word into the CrossWord puzzle as shown.

ACROSS →

1)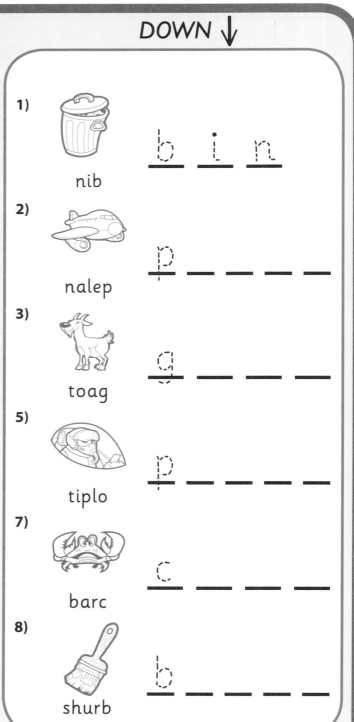
edb

b e d

2)
gip

p _ _

4)
anli

n _ _ _

6)
eablt

t _ _ _ _

7)
ubec

c _ _ _

9)
tepla

p _ _ _ _

DOWN ↓

1)
nib

b i n

2)
nalep

p _ _ _ _

3)
toag

g _ _ _

5)
tiplo

p _ _ _ _

7)
barc

c _ _ _

8)
shurb

b _ _ _ _

 If you are not sure of the answer, simply move on and revisit once a few clues have been completed. **That's all part of the fun!**

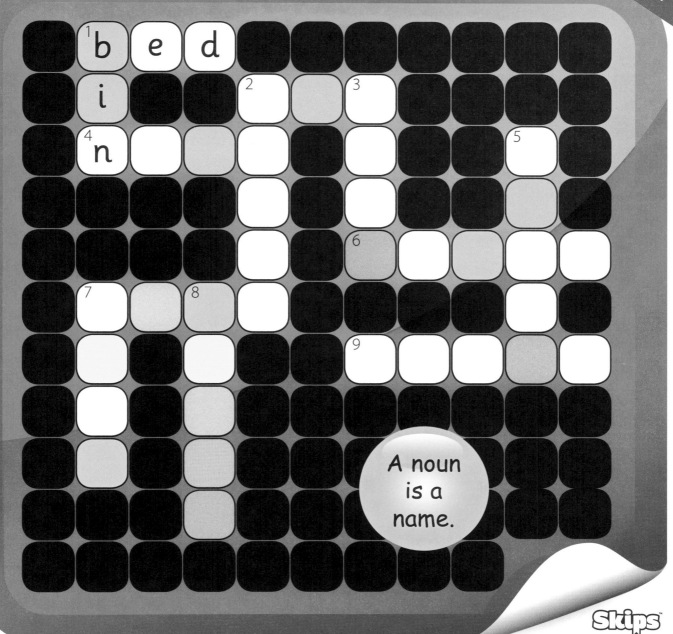

Chapter 1

A noun is a name.

SKIPS CHALLENGE TIME

Well done! Now copy the letters from the coloured tiles in the CrossWord to the matching coloured boxes below and **complete the joke.**

Remember: boxes that are the same colour have the same letter in them.

Q. Have you heard the joke about the dustbin?

A. ◻◻◻ ' ◻   ◻◻◻◻◻◻◻◻ !

Place a SKIPS CHALLENGE sticker here

Well done! It's SKIPS sticker time.

3

VERBS

A VERB is a DOING word.
It is the word that explains what is being done or is happening.

For example: The boy **ran** to school.
"Ran" is a **verb** as it shows what the boy was **doing.**

Below each picture clue are jumbled letters. If you rearrange the letters it will help
you find the VERB. Copy the whole word into the CrossWord puzzle as shown.

ACROSS →

1) cyr
c r y

4) kcki
k _ _ _

6) gisn
s _ _ _

7) keab
b _ _ _

8) poch
c _ _ _

9) lupl
p _ _ _

DOWN ↓

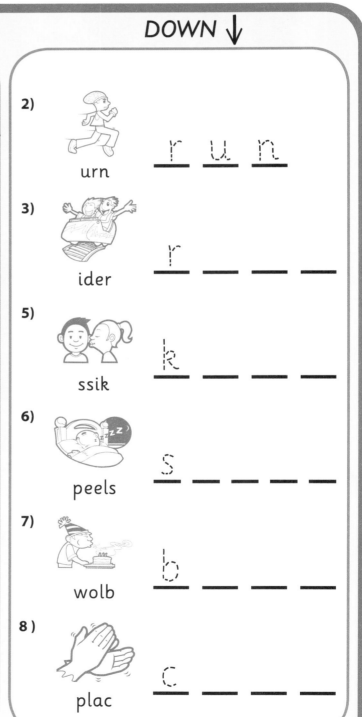

2) urn
r u n

3) ider
r _ _ _

5) ssik
k _ _ _

6) peels
s _ _ _ _

7) wolb
b _ _ _

8) plac
c _ _ _

 If you are not sure of the answer, simply move on and revisit once
a few clues have been completed. **That's all part of the fun!**

Verbs are doing words.

SKIPS CHALLENGE TIME

Well done! Now copy the letters from the coloured tiles in the CrossWord into the matching coloured boxes below and complete the joke.

Remember: boxes that are the same colour have the same letter in them.

Q. Why can't Cinderella play football?

A. Because she ☐☐☐☐ away from the ☐☐☐☐ !

Place a SKIPS CHALLENGE sticker here

Well done! It's SKIPS sticker time.

5

www.skipscrosswords.co.uk

ADJECTIVES

An **ADJECTIVE** is a **DESCRIBING** word.
It is the word that describes what we are talking about in a sentence.

For example: Richard had a **cold** drink.
"Cold" is the **adjective** because it **describes** Richard's drink.

Below each picture clue are jumbled letters. If you rearrange the letters it will help you find the **ADJECTIVE**. Copy the whole word into the CrossWord puzzle as shown.

ACROSS →

1) tew — w e t

3) gib — b _ _

5) voal — o _ _ _

6) tillet — l _ _ _ _ _

9) rgene — g _ _ _ _

10) lewoly — y _ _ _ _ _

DOWN ↓

1) kwea — w e a k

2) allt — t _ _ _

3) uelb — b _ _ _

4) logd — g _ _ _

7) ntih — t _ _ _

8) glyu — u _ _ _

If you are not sure of the answer, simply move on and revisit once a few clues have been completed. **That's all part of the fun!**

Adjectives are describing words.

Skips

SKIPS CHALLENGE TIME

Well done! Now copy the letters from the coloured tiles in the CrossWord into the matching coloured boxes below and **complete the joke.**

Remember: boxes that are the same colour have the same letter in them.

Q. Why is a river so rich?

A. ⬜ ⬜ c ⬜ ⬜ s ⬜　⬜ ⬜

has a ⬜ ⬜ ⬜ ⬜ !

Place a SKIPS CHALLENGE sticker here

Well done! It's SKIPS sticker time.

OPPOSITES (Antonyms)

Words that are OPPOSITE **in meaning are also called** ANTONYMS.

For example: Jane went **up** the hill and Keith went **down** the hill.

In this sentence **"up"** and **"down"** are opposites.

Below each picture clue are jumbled letters. If you rearrange the letters it will help you find the OPPOSITE. Copy the whole word into the CrossWord puzzle as shown.

ACROSS →

1)
ewts

w e s t

3)
nith

t _ _ _

5)
kwal

w _ _ _

7)
astdn

s _ _ _ _

8)
gouny

u _ _ _

9)
pot

t _ _ _

DOWN ↓

1)
ewtih

w h i t e

2)
worth

t _ _ _ _

3)
latl

t _ _ _

4)
ads

s _ _

5)
rowng

w _ _ _ _

6)
grtsno

s _ _ _ _ _

If you are not sure of the answer, simply move on and revisit once a few clues have been completed. **That's all part of the fun!**

8

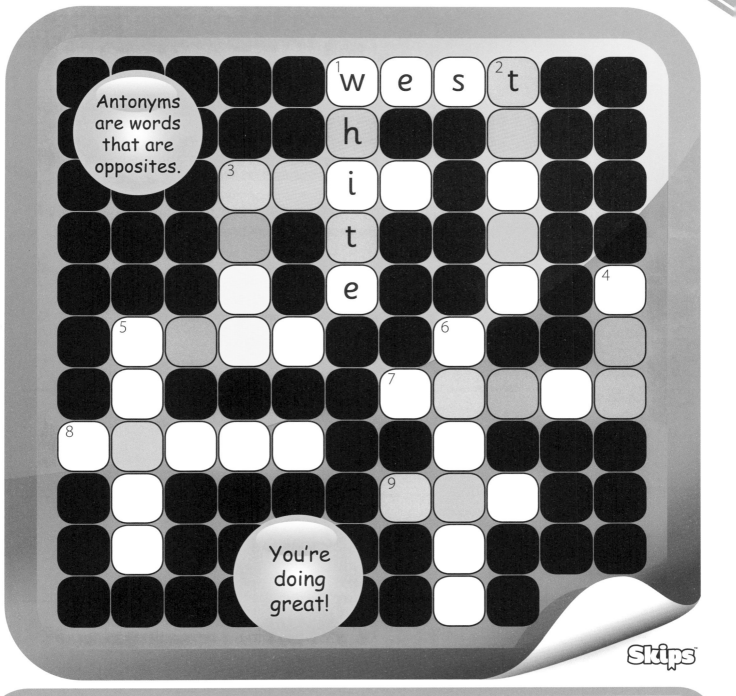

SKIPS CHALLENGE TIME

Well done! Now copy the letters from the coloured tiles in the CrossWord into the matching coloured boxes below and complete the joke.

Remember: boxes that are the same colour have the same letter in them.

Q. Which one is fastest, hot or cold?

A. ☐☐☐, because you can

c ☐ ☐ c ☐ a c ☐ ☐ ☐ !

Place a SKIPS CHALLENGE sticker here

Well done! It's SKIPS sticker time.

MORE THAN ONE (Plurals)

PLURAL means MORE THAN ONE thing.
For example: Chris has one **book**. Sally has two **books**.
In the second sentence **"books"** is plural.

Below each picture clue are jumbled letters. If you rearrange the letters it will help you find the **PLURAL**. Copy the whole word into the CrossWord puzzle as shown.

ACROSS →

1)
sokbo
b o o k s

3) star
tsasr
s _ _ _ _

8) tooth
heett
t _ _ _ _

9) box
xobes
b _ _ _ _

10) vest
tsves
v _ _ _ _

11) snake
sekans
s _ _ _ _ _

DOWN ↓

1)
sbyo
b o y s

2) kite
teiks
k _ _ _ _

4) sheep
peesh
s _ _ _ _

5) foot
teef
f _ _ _

6) baby
biesab
b _ _ _ _ _

7) leaf
sevlea
l _ _ _ _ _

Brilliant!

| b | o | o | k | s |
| o |
| y |
| s |

SKIPS CHALLENGE TIME

Well done! Now copy the letters from the coloured tiles in the CrossWord into the matching coloured boxes below and **complete the joke.**

Remember: boxes that are the same colour have the same letter in them.

Q. What gets bigger the more you take away from it?

A. ▢ ▢▢▢▢ !

Place a SKIPS CHALLENGE sticker here

Well done! It's SKIPS sticker time.

www.skipscrosswords.co.uk

THE ANIMAL KINGDOM

We share our planet with many living things that belong to the animal kingdom.
These include creatures such as dogs, cats, birds, fish and insects.

Below each picture clue are jumbled letters. If you rearrange the letters it will help you find the answer. Copy the whole word into the CrossWord puzzle as shown.

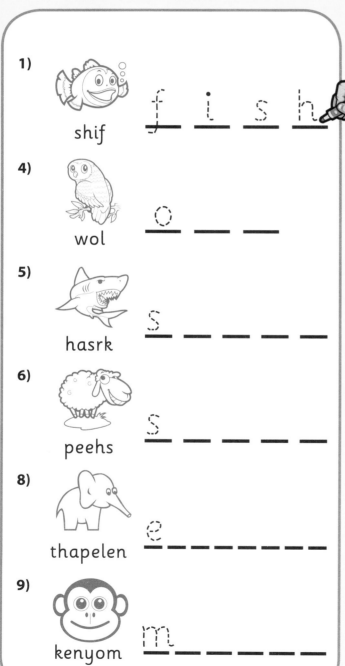

ACROSS →

1) shif — f i s h

4) wol — o _ _

5) hasrk — s _ _ _ _

6) peehs — s _ _ _ _

8) thapelen — e _ _ _ _ _ _ _

9) kenyom — m _ _ _ _ _

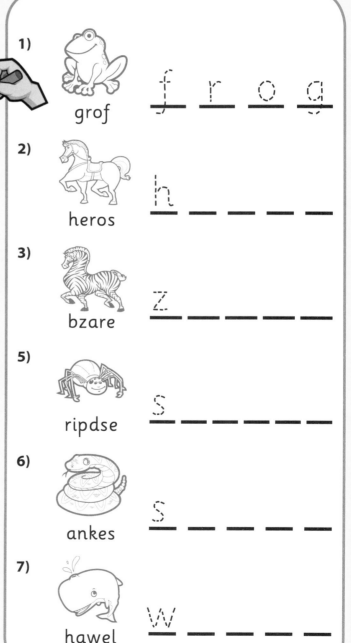

DOWN ↓

1) grof — f r o g

2) heros — h _ _ _ _

3) bzare — z _ _ _ _

5) ripdse — s _ _ _ _ _

6) ankes — s _ _ _ _

7) hawel — w _ _ _ _

 If you are not sure of the answer, simply move on and revisit once a few clues have been completed. **That's all part of the fun!**

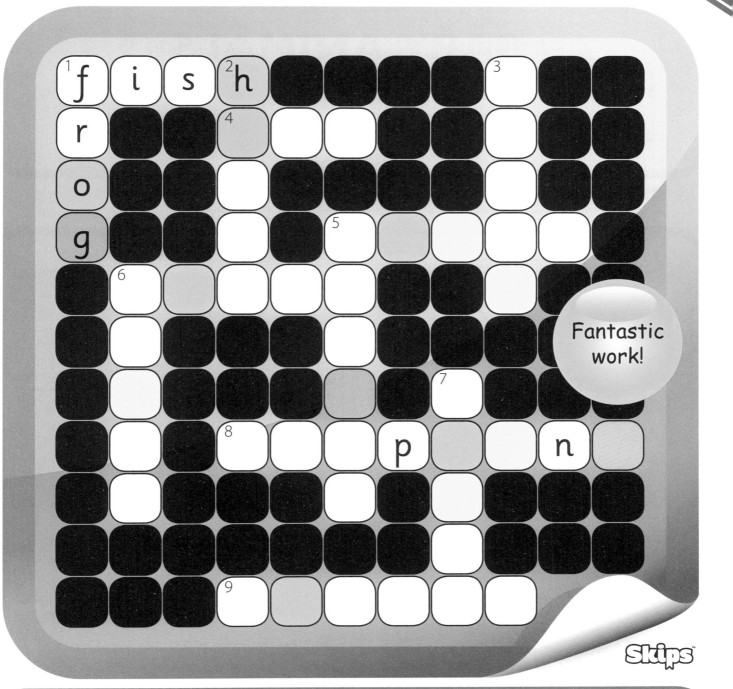

Fantastic work!

Skips

SKIPS CHALLENGE TIME

Well done! Now copy the letters from the coloured tiles in the CrossWord into the matching coloured boxes below and complete the joke.

Remember: boxes that are the same colour have the same letter in them.

Q. What's the only kind of dog you can eat?

A. ☐ ☐☐☐ ☐☐☐ !

Well done! It's SKIPS sticker time.

www.skipscrosswords.co.uk

BABY ANIMALS

A baby is a very young human. Sometimes we give baby animals a special name.

For example: A **foal** is a **baby horse**.
A **baby kangaroo** is called a **joey**.

Below each picture clue are jumbled letters. If you rearrange the letters it will help you find the baby animal. Copy the whole word into the CrossWord puzzle as shown.

ACROSS →

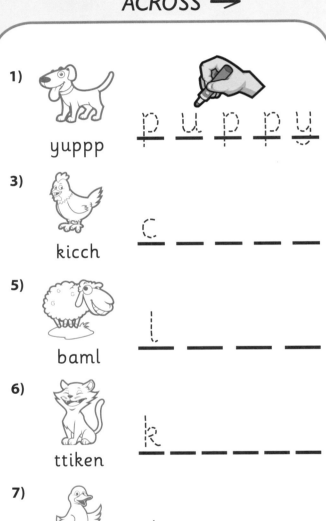

1) p u p p y

yuppp

3) c _ _ _ _

kicch

5) l _ _ _

baml

6) k _ _ _ _

ttiken

7) d _ _ _ _ _ _

dlignuck

DOWN ↓

2) p i g l e t

giptel

3) c _ _

buc

4) c _ _ _

lafc

6) k _ _

dki

8) c _ _

ubc

 If you are not sure of the answer, simply move on and revisit once a few clues have been completed. **That's all part of the fun!**

SKIPS CHALLENGE TIME

Well done! Now copy the letters from the coloured tiles in the CrossWord into the matching coloured boxes below and **complete the joke.**

Remember: boxes that are the same colour have the same letter in them.

Q. What has a head and a tail but no body?

A. ☐ ☐ o ☐ ☐ !

Take your book to school and ask your teacher to put a **WELL DONE SKIP!** sticker here, and there's another one for you.

Great! Show your teacher how well you've done.

PAST AND PRESENT

Things that are HAPPENING NOW are written in the PRESENT tense.
Things that have ALREADY HAPPENED are written in the PAST tense.

For example: Rishi **drinks** some water — this is the present tense.
Rishi **drank** some water — this is the past tense.

Write your answer by filling in the missing letters.
Copy the whole word into the CrossWord puzzle as shown.

ACROSS →

1) Past tense of come (4)

5) Past tense of do (3)

6) Present tense of threw (5)

t _ _ _ _

7) Present tense of bought (3)

b _ _

8) Present tense of swam (5)

s _ _ _ _

10) Present tense of dug (3)

d _ _

DOWN ↓

1) Past tense of climb (7)

2) Present tense of ate (3)

e _ _

3) Past tense of see (3)

s _ _

4) Present tense of drew (4)

d _ _ _

9) Present tense of met (4)

m _ _ _

11) Present tense of gave (4)

g _ _ _

If you are not sure of the answer, simply move on and revisit once a few clues have been completed. **That's all part of the fun!**

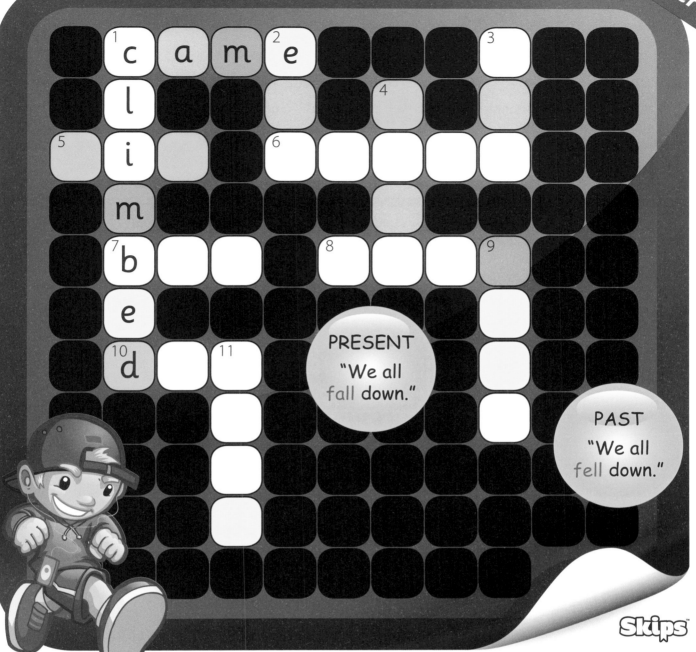

Chapter 2

PRESENT "We all fall down."

PAST "We all fell down."

Skips

SKIPS CHALLENGE TIME

Well done! Now copy the letters from the coloured tiles in the CrossWord into the matching coloured boxes below and **complete the joke**.

Remember: boxes that are the same colour have the same letter in them.

Q. What cheese is made backwards?

A. It's ⬜⬜⬜⬜ !

Place a SKIPS CHALLENGE sticker here

DOUBLE LETTERS

Some words have the same letter TWICE in a row.
These are called DOUBLE LETTERS.

For example: "**Pool**" has a **double "o"**. "**Sorry**" has a **double "r"**.

Write your answer by filling in the missing letters.
Copy the whole word into the CrossWord puzzle as shown.

ACROSS →

1) A colourful talking bird (6)

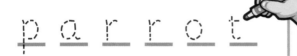

4) Seven days make one of these (4)

5) A sphere shaped object (4)

7) The present tense of fell (4)

9) The number before four (5)

10) An animal with a long neck (7)

DOWN ↓

1) Present tense of pulled (4)

2) A furry pet with long ears that likes carrots (6)

3) Present tense of felt (4)

6) A motor truck (5)

7) Plural (more than one) of foot (4)

8) Another word for small (6)

If you are not sure of the answer, simply move on and revisit once a few clues have been completed. **That's all part of the fun!**

for more SKIPS titles visit our website

SKIPS CHALLENGE TIME

Well done! Now copy the letters from the coloured tiles in the CrossWord into the matching coloured boxes below and complete the joke.

Remember: boxes that are the same colour have the same letter in them.

Q. Which room doesn't have any windows?

A. ☐ m ☐ s ☐ ☐ ☐ ☐ m !

Place a SKIPS CHALLENGE sticker here

Well done! It's SKIPS sticker time.

www.skipscrosswords.co.uk

ALPHABETICAL ORDER

You may already know the **alphabet**, it begins with **a** and ends with **z**.
If you put words in alphabetical order, then they follow the same order as the **alphabet**.

a b c d e f g h i j k l m n o p q r s t u v w x y z

One of these words is **not** in alphabetical order. Write the word as your answer.
Copy the whole word into the CrossWord puzzle as shown.

ACROSS →

2) bear frog goat duck swan (4)

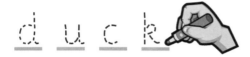

5) bulb lamp plug wood door (4)

_ _ _ _

7) foul trap goal kick pass (4)

_ _ _ _

9) fast stop goes runs walk (4)

_ _ _ _

10) drop flag pull spin cost (4)

_ _ _ _

11) ship skin soil sail swim (4)

s _ _ _

DOWN ↓

1) wait fall meet runs sits (4)

w a i t

3) hours month times clock years (5)

_ _ _ _ _

4) board print draws rings write (5)

_ _ _ _ _

6) rips snip tear wrap chop (4)

_ _ _ _

8) post crab fall shop tall (4)

_ _ _ _

9) shine smile split skirt stink (5)

s _ _ _ _

If you are not sure of the answer, simply move on and revisit once a few clues have been completed. **That's all part of the fun!**

for more SKIPS titles visit our website

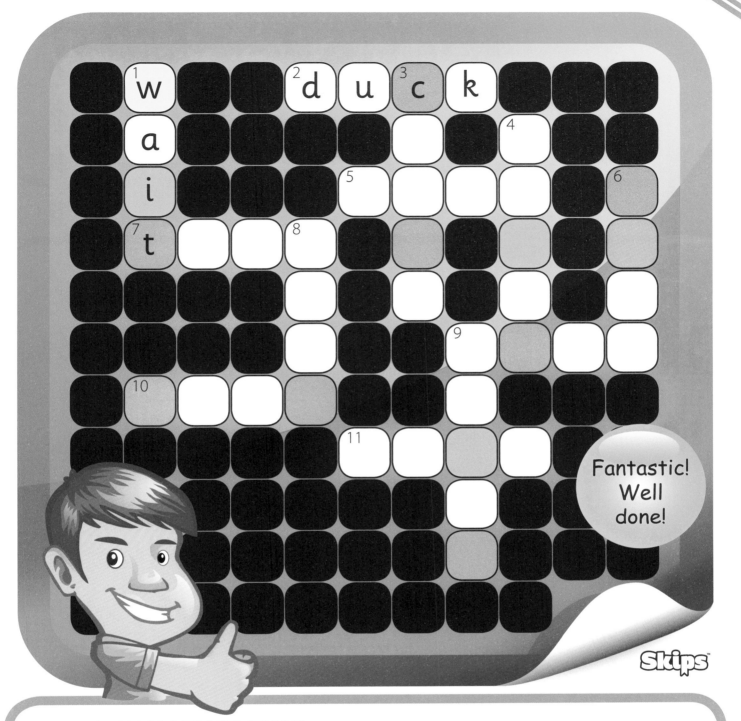

SKIPS CHALLENGE TIME

Well done! Now copy the letters from the coloured tiles in the CrossWord into the matching coloured boxes below and complete the joke.

Remember: boxes that are the same colour have the same letter in them.

Q. Why did the twin witches wear name badges?

A. So they could tell ☐☐☐☐☐

☐☐☐☐☐ was ☐☐☐☐☐ !

Place a SKIPS CHALLENGE sticker here

Well done! It's SKIPS sticker time.

SIMILAR WORDS (Synonyms)

Words that MEAN THE SAME **are called** SYNONYMS.

For example: "**quick**" and "**fast**"

Both words have **similar meanings** — they are synonyms.

Write your answer by filling in the missing letters.
Copy the whole word into the CrossWord puzzle as shown.

ACROSS →

1) Pain (4)

h u r t

5) Talk (5)

s _ _ _ k

7) Wealthy (4)

r _ _ _

8) Halt (4)

s _ _ _

10) Start (5)

b _ _ _ _

11) Enjoy (4)

l _ k _

DOWN ↓

2) Hurry (4)

r u s h

3) Big (5)

l _ _ g _

4) Present (4)

g _ _ _

6) Circular (5)

r _ _ _ d

8) Painful (4)

s _ r _

9) Tug (4)

p _ _ _

 If you are not sure of the answer, simply move on and revisit once a few clues have been completed. **That's all part of the fun!**

Synonyms are words that mean the same.

Great work!

Skips

SKIPS CHALLENGE TIME

Well done! Now copy the letters from the coloured tiles in the CrossWord into the matching coloured boxes below and complete the joke.

Remember: boxes that are the same colour have the same letter in them.

Q. What did the baker say when he lost his cake?

A. ☐☐ ' ☐ ☐☐☐☐☐ !

Take your book to school and ask your teacher to put a **WELL DONE SKIP!** sticker here, and there's another one for you.

Great! Show your teacher how well you've done.

SOUNDS THE SAME (Homophones)

Some words SOUND THE SAME but are spelt differently and have totally different meanings — they are called HOMOPHONES.

For example: **"red"** and **"read"** are homophones.
"son" and **"sun"** are homophones.

Write your answer by filling in the missing letters.
Copy the whole word into the CrossWord puzzle as shown.

ACROSS →   DOWN ↓

1) Blue (4)

 b l e w

5) Won (3)

 o _ _

6) Write (5)

r _ _ _ _

8) Hair (4)

h _ _ _

9) Knight (5)

n _ _ _ _

11) Stair (5)

s _ _ r _

2) Ate (5)

 e i g h t

3) For (4)

f _ _ _

4) Sea (3)

s _ _

6) Red (4)

r _ _ _

7) There (5)

t _ _ i _

10) Our (4)

h _ _ _

If you are not sure of the answer, simply move on and revisit once a few clues have been completed. **That's all part of the fun!**

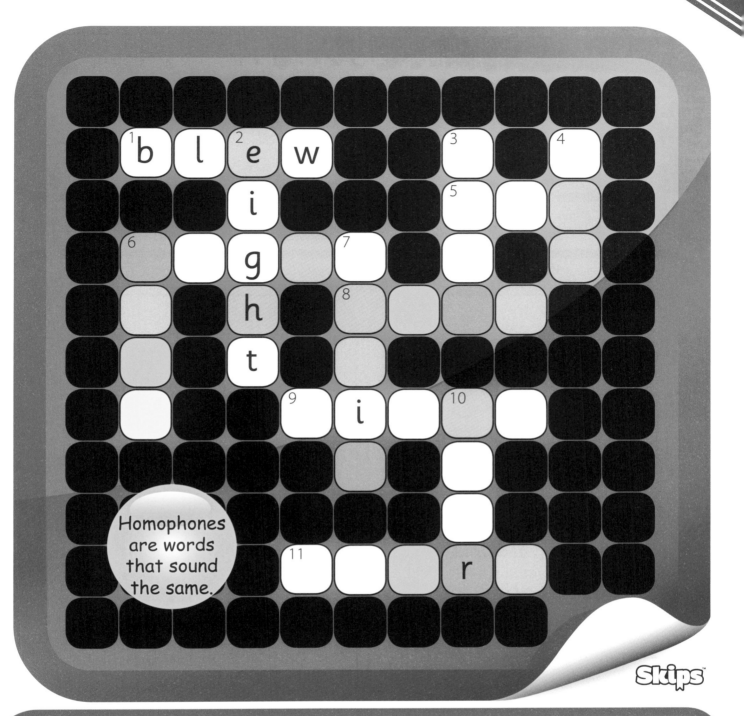

Homophones are words that sound the same.

Skips

SKIPS CHALLENGE TIME

Well done! Now copy the letters from the coloured tiles in the CrossWord into the matching coloured boxes below and **complete the joke**.

Remember: boxes that are the same colour have the same letter in them.

Q. Why did the man put a rabbit on his head?

A. Because he ☐☐☐

no ☐☐☐☐ !

Place a SKIPS CHALLENGE sticker here

Well done! It's SKIPS sticker time.

25

AROUND THE HOUSE

This CrossWord is about things that you might find in your house.

The answers are all NOUNS.

For example: A **sink** is a **noun**. A **mug** is a **noun**.

Write your answer by filling in the missing letters.
Copy the whole word into the CrossWord puzzle as shown.

ACROSS →

1) Something you sleep on (3)

b e d

4) You use this to eat soup with (5)

s _ _ _ _

6) You keep food and drink in this to keep them cool (6)

f _ _ _ g _

7) Something you switch on to give you light (4)

l _ _ _

9) Made of metal, it has a handle and you heat food in it (3)

p _ _

10) You can sit on this (5)

c _ _ _ _

DOWN ↓

1) You throw rubbish into it (3)

b i n

2) You open and close this to go between rooms (4)

d _ _ _

3) Cloth used to dry yourself after a bath (5)

t _ _ _ _

5) You can drink tea from this (3)

c _ _

6) On a hot day this helps you to keep cool (3)

f _ _

8) You can see your reflection in this (6)

m _ _ r _ r

If you are not sure of the answer, simply move on and revisit once a few clues have been completed. **That's all part of the fun!**

Great work!

Skips

Q. What did the fast tomato say to the slow tomato?

A. You go ahead, ⬜'⬜⬜

k⬜⬜⬜⬜⬜⬜ !

Place a SKIPS CHALLENGE sticker here

PARTS OF THE BODY

This CrossWord is all about parts of the human body.

The answers are all NOUNS.

For example: An **arm** is a noun. A **heart** is a noun.

Write your answer by filling in the missing letters.
Copy the whole word into the CrossWord puzzle as shown.

ACROSS →

1) Helps you to think? (5)

 b r a i n

5) These help you to see (4)

e _ _ _

6) The back part of a foot (4)

h _ _ _

7) You have five of these on each foot (4)

t _ _ _

9) You kick a ball with this (4)

f _ _ _

11) Has nostrils and is part of your face (4)

n _ _ _

DOWN ↓

2) Connects the foot to the leg (5)

a n k l e

3) Connects your head to your shoulders (4)

n _ _ _

4) Use for biting and chewing (5)

t _ _ _ _

8) Part of your arm (5)

e _ _ _ w

9) A closed hand makes this (4)

f _ _ _

10) The part that helps your leg to bend (4)

k _ _ _

 If you are not sure of the answer, simply move on and revisit once a few clues have been completed. **That's all part of the fun!**

SKIPS CHALLENGE TIME

Well done! Now copy the letters from the coloured tiles in the CrossWord into the matching coloured boxes below and complete the joke.

Remember: boxes that are the same colour have the same letter in them.

Q. What is a skeleton's favourite food?

A. ☐ p ☐ ☐ ☐   ☐ ☐ ☐ ☐ !

Place a SKIPS CHALLENGE sticker here

TIME

Time is how we measure how long something lasts.

For instance: A **year** is normally **365 days**, made up of **12 months** or **52 weeks**. There are **7 days** in a week, **24 hours** in a day, **60 minutes** in an hour and **60 seconds** in a minute.

Write your answer by filling in the missing letters.
Copy the whole word into the CrossWord puzzle as shown.

ACROSS →

1) 60 seconds make one of these (6)

2) 12 months make one of these (4)

5) The month after January (8)

6) 24 hours make one of these (3)

8) The month before September (6)

9) The month after June (4)

DOWN ↓

1) The month after April (3)

3) The month after March (5)

4) A weekend day (8)

S _ _ _ _ _ _ _

5) The day after Thursday (6)

F _ _ _ _ _

7) Sixty minutes make one of these (4)

If you are not sure of the answer, simply move on and revisit once a few clues have been completed. **That's all part of the fun!**

Great work, keep it up!

Skips

CrossWord Practice 1

Practice makes perfect! To get really good at something you need to practise.

The numbers in the bracket at the end of each clue tells you how many letters are in the correct answer. The first ones have been done for you.

ACROSS →

1) An animal you can ride (5)

4) Is a name a verb or a noun? (4)

6) The plural (more than one) of man (3)

7) Sounds the same as the letter "I" (3)

8) Opposite (antonym) of far (4)

9) What will an angry wasp do? (5)

10) A person who cooks for other people (4)

13) What is the plural (more than one) of baby (6)

DOWN ↓

1) Antonym (opposite) of sad (5)

2) Past tense of run (3)

3) The lower part of your face (4)

5) This is a colour and a fruit (6)

6) The month after February (5)

7) Synonym (similar) of simple (4)

11) Which word is in the wrong alphabetical order:
   fuss face feet fish flip

12) The month after April (3)

If you are not sure of the answer, simply move on and revisit once a few clues have been completed. **That's all part of the fun!**

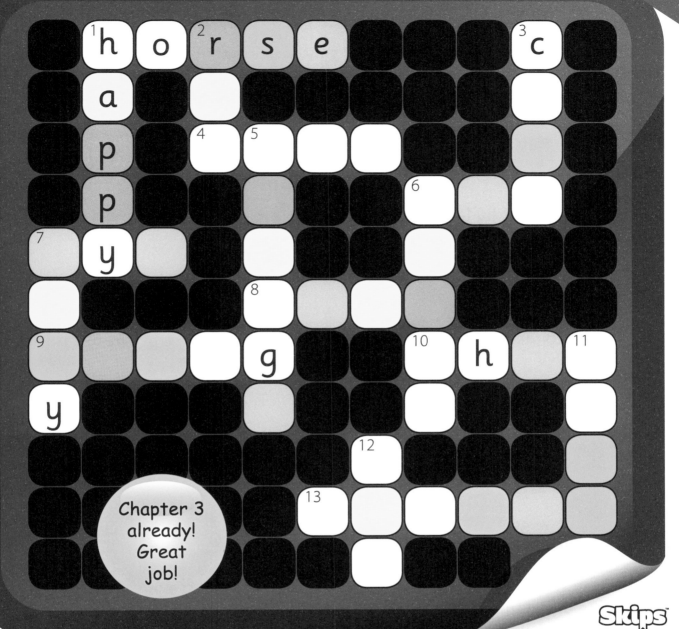

Chapter 3 already! Great job!

Skips

SKIPS CHALLENGE TIME

Well done! Now copy the letters from the coloured tiles in the CrossWord into the matching coloured boxes below and **complete the joke**.

Remember: boxes that are the same colour have the same letter in them.

Q. What is the twins Sacha and Rishi's favourite fruit?

A. ⬜⬜ ' ⬜ ⬜ ⬜⬜⬜⬜ !

Place a SKIPS CHALLENGE sticker here

CrossWord Practice 2

Practice makes perfect! **To get really good at something you need to practise.**

The numbers in the bracket at the end of each clue tells you how many letters are in the correct answer. The first ones have been done for you.

ACROSS →

2) Past tense of fly (4)

3) Homophone (sounds the same) of road (4)

6) 60 seconds make one of these (6)

7) A table has one of these on each corner (3)

9) Is the word "playing" a noun or a verb? (4)

11) Which word is in the wrong alphabetical order:
baby bone best bite bush

12) The plural (more than one) of leaf? (6)

13) What is the past tense of now? (4)

DOWN ↓

1) A long handled brush (5)

2) The month after January (8)

4) A person who looks after sick people (5)

5) The antonym (opposite) of no (3)

8) A traffic light colour (5)

9) What you put flowers in (4)

10) Synonym (similar meaning) of quick (4)

11) Homophone (sounds the same) of blew (4)

If you are not sure of the answer, simply move on and revisit once a few clues have been completed. **That's all part of the fun!**

for more SKIPS titles visit our website

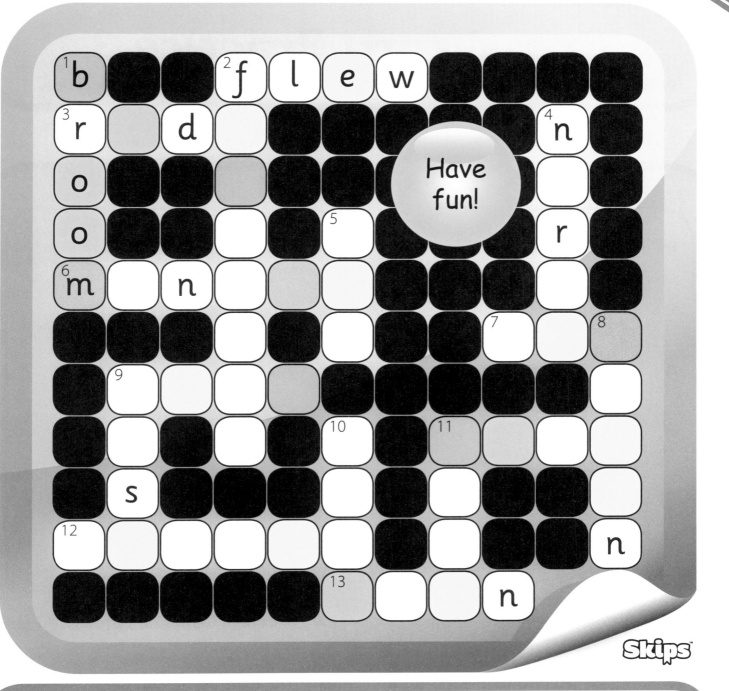

SKIPS CHALLENGE TIME

Well done! Now copy the letters from the coloured tiles in the CrossWord into the matching coloured boxes below and complete the joke.

Remember: boxes that are the same colour have the same letter in them.

Q. Why did the toilet paper roll down the hill?

A. To ☐☐☐ to the

☐☐☐☐☐☐ !

Place a SKIPS CHALLENGE sticker here

Well done! It's SKIPS sticker time.

35

CrossWord Practice 3

Practice makes perfect! **To get really good at something you need to practise.**

The numbers in the bracket at the end of each clue tells you how many letters are in the correct answer. The first ones have been done for you.

ACROSS →

1) The warmest season of the year (6)

4) Homophone (sounds the same) of ate (5)

7) Is the word "draw" a verb or a noun? (4)

9) A shape with curved edges (4)

10) Past tense of throw (5)

11) The month after March (5)

14) Antonym (opposite) of black (5)

15) This is used to boil water in (6)

DOWN ↓

2) The month after February (5)

3) A colour you see on traffic lights (3)

5) The past tense of give (4)

6) Synonym (similar) of high (4)

8) 12 months make one of these (4)

11) A little insect (3)

12) Antonym (opposite) of found (4)

13) The joint in the middle of your leg (4)

If you are not sure of the answer, simply move on and revisit once a few clues have been completed. **That's all part of the fun!**

for more SKIPS titles visit our website

	s¹	u	m²	m	e	r³				
			a			⁴	⁵		⁶
⁷			r						
			c		⁸	⁹o		l
	¹⁰	h					l
			¹¹			¹²		¹³
¹⁴							
				¹⁵		t	
You're doing brilliantly!						

SKIPS CHALLENGE TIME

Well done! Now copy the letters from the coloured tiles in the CrossWord into the matching coloured boxes below and **complete the joke.**

Remember: boxes that are the same colour have the same letter in them.

Q. What do you call a deer without any eyes?

A. I have ▢▢ ▢▢▢▢ !

Place a SKIPS CHALLENGE sticker here

CrossWord Practice 4

Practice makes perfect! **To get really good at something you need to practise.**

The numbers in the bracket at the end of each clue tells you how many letters are in the correct answer. The first ones have been done for you.

ACROSS →

1) A heavy metal object that stops a ship from moving (6)

3) Where a baby sleeps (3)

4) A large wild cat (5)

7) A yellow fruit (5)

8) Furniture you can sit on (5)

10) You put cakes in this to bake (4)

11) Homophone (sounds the same) of read (3)

DOWN ↓

1) A fruit (5)

2) Something you wear on your head (3)

3) These are hung in windows (8)

5) A person who delivers letters (7)

6) The day after Thursday (6)

9) The sound a lion makes (4)

12) 24 hours make one of these (3)

 If you are not sure of the answer, simply move on and revisit once a few clues have been completed. **That's all part of the fun!**

SKIPS CHALLENGE TIME

Well done! Now copy the letters from the coloured tiles in the CrossWord into the matching coloured boxes below to **complete the joke.**

Remember: boxes that are the same colour have the same letter in them.

Q. Where do books sleep?

A. ☐☐☐☐☐ their

☐☐☐☐☐☐ !

Take your book to school and ask your teacher to put a **WELL DONE SKIP!** sticker here, and there's another one for you.

Great! Show your teacher how well you've done.

39

www.skipscrosswords.co.uk

CrossWord Practice 5

Practice makes perfect! **To get really good at something you need to practise.**

The numbers in the bracket at the end of each clue tells you how many letters are in the correct answer. The first ones have been done for you.

ACROSS →

1) Is "chair" a verb or a noun? (4)

4) Antonym (opposite) of far (4)

6) Past tense of eat (3)

8) A farmyard animal (3)

9) The plural (more than one) of tooth (5)

11) Present tense of had (4)

12) A kitten is a baby of which animal? (3)

15) Large animal with a trunk (8)

DOWN ↓

1) Antonym (opposite) of all (4)

2) The coldest season (6)

3) Homophone (sounds the same) of bear (4)

5) Antonym (opposite) of left (5)

7) The plural (more than one) of story (7)

10) Part of your foot (3)

13) A person who helps sick animals to get better (3)

14) Antonym (opposite) of thin (3)

 If you are not sure of the answer, simply move on and revisit once a few clues have been completed. **That's all part of the fun!**

for more SKIPS titles visit our website

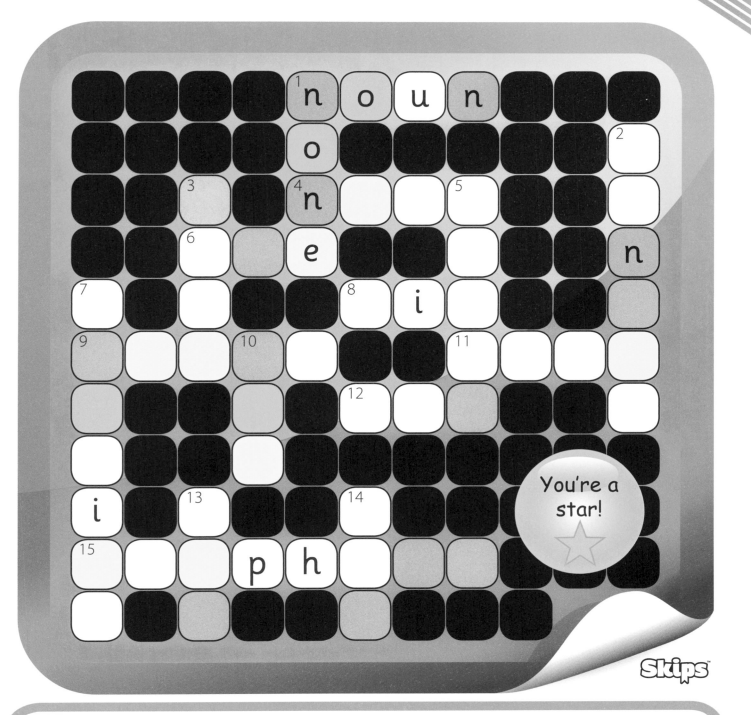

SKIPS CHALLENGE TIME

Well done! Now copy the letters from the coloured tiles in the CrossWord into the matching coloured boxes below and complete the joke.

Remember: boxes that are the same colour have the same letter in them.

Q. Why can't cars play football?

A. They only have

 !

Place a SKIPS CHALLENGE sticker here

Well done! It's SKIPS sticker time.

www.skipscrosswords.co.uk

CrossWord Practice 6

Practice makes perfect! **To get really good at something you need to practise.**

The numbers in the bracket at the end of each clue tells you how many letters are in the correct answer. The first ones have been done for you.

ACROSS →

1) Homophone (sounds the same) of no (4)

2) Part of the body below the ankle (4)

5) A group of puppies (6)

6) The month before April (5)

8) A group of bees (5)

10) Homophone (sounds the same) of bare (4)

11) A weekend day (6)

DOWN ↓

1) Plural (more than one) of knife (6)

2) A number between one and ten (4)

3) Homophone (sounds the same) of toe (3)

4) Part of your body connected to your shoulder (3)

7) Opposite (antonym) of light (5)

9) Part of your face (5)

12) At night it gets _ _ _ _ (4)

 If you are not sure of the answer, simply move on and revisit once a few clues have been completed. **That's all part of the fun!**

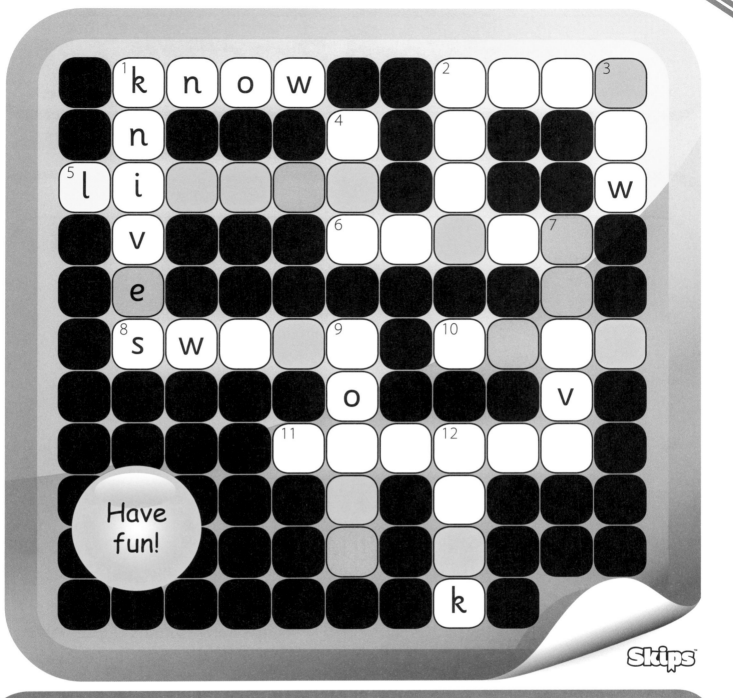

SKIPS CHALLENGE TIME

Well done! Now copy the letters from the coloured tiles in the CrossWord into the matching coloured boxes below to complete the joke.

Remember: boxes that are the same colour have the same letter in them.

Q. What do you find in the middle of nowhere?

A. The ⬜⬜⬜⬜⬜⬜ " ⬜ " !

Take your book to school and ask your teacher to put a **WELL DONE SKIP!** sticker here, and there's another one for you.

Great! Show your teacher how well you've done.

43

www.skipscrosswords.co.uk

CrossWord Practice 7

Practice makes perfect! To get really good at something you need to practise.

The numbers in the bracket at the end of each clue tells you how many letters are in the correct answer. The first ones have been done for you.

ACROSS →

1) Past tense of drink (5)

2) Wood is this colour (5)

4) You find treasure in this (5)

7) The liquid inside a pen (3)

8) Homophone (sounds the same) of won (3)

9) What does a band play? (5)

10) Past tense of know (4)

13) Used to stop water going down the hole in a sink (4)

DOWN ↓

1) The Christmas month (8)

2) The noise a dog makes (4)

3) The day after Tuesday (9)

5) Antonym (opposite) of west (4)

6) This shows that something is correct (4)

11) Homophone (sounds the same) of knight (5)

12) Homophone (sounds the same) of waste (5)

13) A purple fruit (4)

If you are not sure of the answer, simply move on and revisit once a few clues have been completed. **That's all part of the fun!**

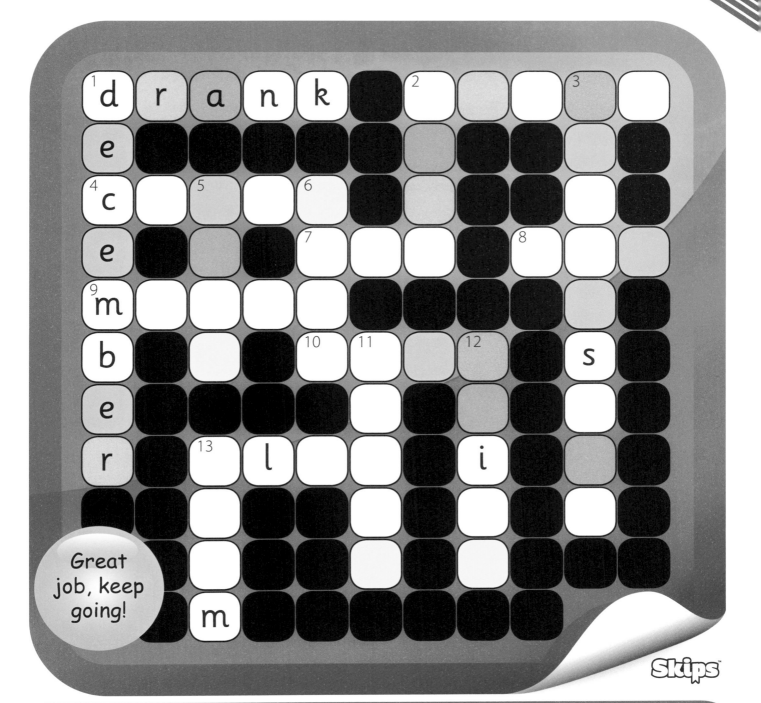

Great job, keep going!

Skips

SKIPS CHALLENGE TIME

Well done! Now copy the letters from the coloured tiles in the CrossWord into the matching coloured boxes below to complete the joke.

Remember: boxes that are the same colour have the same letter in them.

Q. What runs but never walks?

A. ⬜⬜⬜⬜⬜ !

Place a SKIPS CHALLENGE sticker here

Well done! It's SKIPS sticker time.

CrossWord Practice 8

Practice makes perfect! **To get really good at something you need to practise.**

The numbers in the bracket at the end of each clue tells you how many letters are in the correct answer. The first ones have been done for you.

ACROSS →

1) Plural (more than one) of woman (5)

5) Homophone (sounds the same) of not (4)

6) A grown up person (5)

7) Wife of a king (5)

9) The day after yesterday (5)

11) Antonym (opposite) of here (5)

12) A person who treats teeth (7)

DOWN ↓

1) Past tense of win (5)

2) Wife of a father (6)

3) 60 minutes make one of these (4)

4) Antonym (opposite) of in (3)

6) Wife of an uncle (4)

8) A person who bakes cakes and bread (5)

10) Antonym (opposite) of closed (4)

11) Homophone (sounds the same) of tyre (4)

If you are not sure of the answer, simply move on and revisit once a few clues have been completed. **That's all part of the fun!**

for more SKIPS titles visit our website

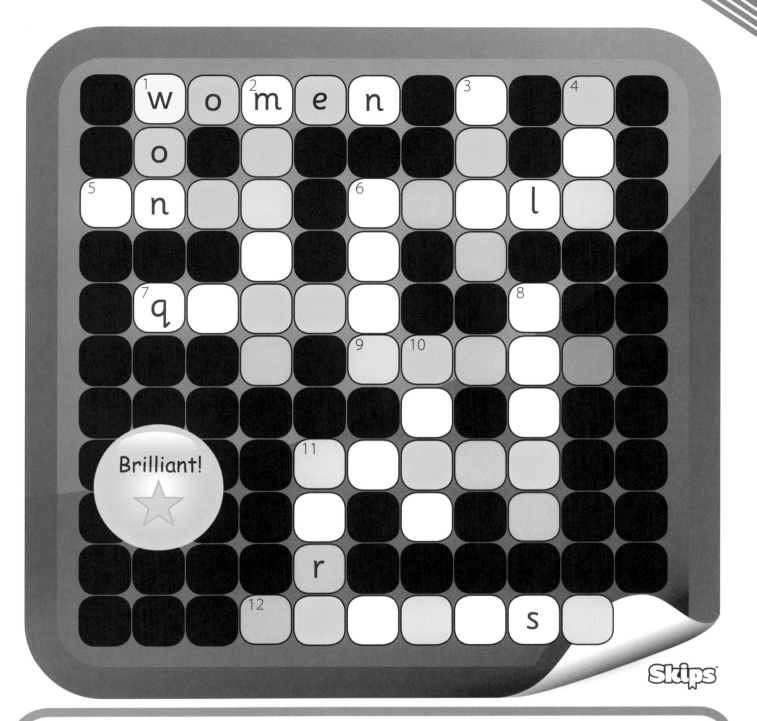

Brilliant! ⭐

Skips

SKIPS CHALLENGE TIME

Well done! Now copy the letters from the coloured tiles in the CrossWord into the matching coloured boxes below and complete the joke.

Remember: boxes that are the same colour have the same letter in them.

Q. Why can't a bicycle stand up?

A. Because it's

☐☐☐ ☐☐☐☐☐☐ !

Place a SKIPS CHALLENGE sticker here

CrossWord Practice 9

Practice makes perfect! **To get really good at something you need to practise.**

The numbers in the bracket at the end of each clue tells you how many letters are in the correct answer. The first ones have been done for you.

ACROSS →

1) An insect with large colourful wings (9)

4) This is inside your mouth, you use it to speak (6)

7) You use these to listen (4)

8) To have a lot of money (4)

9) Opposite (antonym) of east (4)

10) Homophone (sounds the same) of our (4)

13) There are four of these in a year (7)

15) Plural (more than one) of leaf (6)

DOWN ↓

2) Use this to brush your teeth (10)

3) When something costs nothing (4)

5) Used for sticking things (4)

6) The joint where your hand meets your arm (5)

9) Antonym (opposite) of dry (3)

11) Synonym (similar) of above (4)

12) _ _ _ _ upon a time (4)

14) Homophone (sounds the same) of won (3)

You're now ready to move up to the next SKIPS book.

If you are not sure of the answer, simply move on and revisit once a few clues have been completed. **That's all part of the fun!**

This is the final puzzle! Well Done Skip!

Skips

Q. Why can you now eat your **SKIPS** book?

A. Because it's a ⬡p⬡⬡⬡⬡

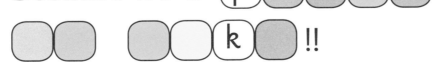

⬡⬡ ⬡⬡k⬡ !!

Take your book to school and ask your teacher to put a **WELL DONE SKIP!** sticker here, and there's another one for you.

Great! Show your teacher how well you've done.

ANSWERS

Well done! Now check your answers and see how many questions you answered correctly.

Good luck!

Page 2-3   Nouns

ACROSS		DOWN	
1	bed	1	bin
2	pig	2	plane
4	nail	3	goat
6	table	5	pilot
7	cube	7	crab
9	plate	8	brush

SKIPS CHALLENGE

Q. Have you heard the joke about the dustbin?

A. i t ' s   r u b b i s h !

Page 4-5   Verbs

ACROSS		DOWN	
1	cry	2	run
4	kick	3	ride
6	sing	5	kiss
7	bake	6	sleep
8	chop	7	blow
9	pull	8	clap

SKIPS CHALLENGE

Q. Why can't Cinderella play football?

A. Because she r u n s away from the b a l l !

Page 6-7   Adjectives

ACROSS		DOWN	
1	wet	1	weak
3	big	2	tall
5	oval	3	blue
6	little	4	gold
9	green	7	thin
10	yellow	8	ugly

SKIPS CHALLENGE

Q. Why is a river so rich?

A. b e c a u s e   i t has a b a n k !

Page 8-9   Opposites (Antonyms)

ACROSS		DOWN	
1	west	1	white
3	thin	2	throw
5	walk	3	tall
7	stand	4	sad
8	young	5	wrong
9	top	6	strong

SKIPS CHALLENGE

Q. Which one is fastest, hot or cold?

A. h o t , because you can c a t c h a c o l d !

Page 10-11   More Than One (Plurals)

ACROSS		DOWN	
1	books	1	boys
3	stars	2	kites
8	teeth	4	sheep
9	boxes	5	feet
10	vests	6	babies
11	snakes	7	leaves

SKIPS CHALLENGE

Q. What gets bigger the more you take away from it?

A. a h o l e !

Page 12-13   The Animal Kingdom

ACROSS		DOWN	
1	fish	1	frog
4	owl	2	horse
5	shark	3	zebra
6	sheep	5	spider
8	elephant	6	snake
9	monkey	7	whale

SKIPS CHALLENGE

Q. What's the only kind of dog you can eat?

A. a h o t d o g !

Page 14-15   Baby Animals

ACROSS		DOWN	
1	puppy	2	piglet
3	chick	3	cub
5	lamb	4	calf
6	kitten	6	kid
7	duckling	8	cub

SKIPS CHALLENGE

Q. What has a head and a tail but no body?

A. a c o i n !

Page 16-17   Past and Present

ACROSS		DOWN	
1	came	1	climbed
5	did	2	eat
6	throw	3	saw
7	buy	4	draw
8	swim	9	meet
10	dig	11	give

SKIPS CHALLENGE

Q. What cheese is made backwards?

A. It's e d a m !

Page 18-19   Double Letters

ACROSS		DOWN	
1	parrot	1	pull
4	week	2	rabbit
5	ball	3	feel
7	fall	6	lorry
9	three	7	feet
10	giraffe	8	little

SKIPS CHALLENGE

Q. Which room doesn't have any windows?

A. a m u s h r o o m !

Page 20-21   Alphabetical Order

ACROSS		DOWN	
2	duck	1	wait
5	door	3	clock
7	trap	4	print
9	stop	6	chop
10	cost	8	post
11	sail	9	skirt

SKIPS CHALLENGE

Q. Why did the twin witches wear name badges?

A. So they could tell w h i c h w i t c h was w h i c h !

Page 22-23 Similar Words (Synonyms)

ACROSS		DOWN	
1	hurt	2	rush
5	speak	3	large
7	rich	4	gift
8	stop	6	round
10	begin	8	sore
11	like	9	pull

SKIPS CHALLENGE

Q. What did the baker say when he lost his cake?

A. **i t** 's **s c o n e** !

Page 24-25 Sounds the Same (Homophones)

ACROSS		DOWN	
1	blew	2	eight
5	one	3	four
6	right	4	see
8	hare	6	read
9	night	7	their
11	stare	10	hour

SKIPS CHALLENGE

Q. Why did the man put a rabbit on his head?

A. Because he **h a d** no **h a r e** !

Page 26-27 Around the House

ACROSS		DOWN	
1	bed	1	bin
4	spoon	2	door
6	fridge	3	towel
7	lamp	5	cup
9	pan	6	fan
10	chair	8	mirror

SKIPS CHALLENGE

Q. What did the fast tomato say to the slow tomato?

A. You go ahead, **I** ' **l l**
k e t c h u p !

Page 28-29 Parts of the Body

ACROSS		DOWN	
1	brain	2	ankle
5	eyes	3	neck
6	heel	4	teeth
7	toes	8	elbow
9	foot	9	fist
11	nose	10	knee

SKIPS CHALLENGE

Q. What is a skeleton's favourite food?

A. **s p a r e r i b s** !

Page 30-31 Time

ACROSS		DOWN	
1	minute	1	May
2	year	3	April
5	February	4	Saturday
6	day	5	Friday
8	August	7	hour
9	July		

SKIPS CHALLENGE

Q. What's the best day to go to the beach?

A. **s u n d a y** of course!

Page 32-33 CrossWord Practice 1

ACROSS		DOWN	
1	horse	1	happy
4	noun	2	ran
6	men	3	chin
7	eye	5	orange
8	near	6	March
9	sting	7	easy
10	chef	11	fuss
13	babies	12	May

SKIPS CHALLENGE

Q. What is the twins Sacha and Rishi's favourite fruit?

A. **i t** 's **a p e a r** !

for more SKIPS titles visit our website

Page 34-35 CrossWord Practice 2

ACROSS		DOWN	
2	flew	1	broom
3	rode	2	February
6	minute	4	nurse
7	leg	5	yes
9	verb	8	green
10	bone	9	vase
12	leaves	10	fast
13	then	11	blue

SKIPS CHALLENGE

Q. Why did the toilet paper roll down the hill?

A. To **g e t** to the **b o t t o m** !

Page 36-37 CrossWord Practice 3

ACROSS		DOWN	
1	summer	2	March
4	eight	3	red
7	verb	5	gave
9	oval	6	tall
10	threw	8	year
11	April	11	ant
14	white	12	lost
15	kettle	13	knee

SKIPS CHALLENGE

Q. What do you call a deer without any eyes?

A. I have **n o** **i d e a** !

Page 38-39 CrossWord Practice 4

ACROSS		DOWN	
1	anchor	1	apple
3	cot	2	hat
4	tiger	3	curtains
7	lemon	5	postman
8	chair	6	Friday
10	oven	9	roar
11	red	12	day

SKIPS CHALLENGE

Q. Where do books sleep?

A. **u n d e r** their **c o v e r s** !

Page 40-41 CrossWord Practice 5

ACROSS		DOWN	
1	noun	1	none
4	near	2	winter
6	ate	3	bare
8	pig	5	right
9	teeth	7	stories
11	have	10	toe
12	cat	13	vet
15	elephant	14	fat

SKIPS CHALLENGE

Q. Why can't cars play football?

A. They only have **o n e** **b o o t** !

Page 42-43 CrossWord Practice 6

ACROSS		DOWN	
1	know	1	knives
2	foot	2	four
5	litter	3	tow
6	March	4	arm
8	swarm	7	heavy
10	bear	9	mouth
11	Sunday	12	dark

SKIPS CHALLENGE

Q. What do you find in the middle of nowhere?

A. The **l e t t e r** "**h**" !

Page 44-45 CrossWord Practice 7

ACROSS		DOWN	
1	drank	1	December
2	brown	2	bark
4	chest	3	Wednesday
7	ink	5	east
8	one	6	tick
9	music	11	night
10	knew	12	waist
13	plug	13	plum

SKIPS CHALLENGE

Q. What runs but never walks?

A. **w a t e r** !

Page 46-47 CrossWord Practice 8

ACROSS		DOWN	
1	women	1	won
5	knot	2	mother
6	adult	3	hour
7	queen	4	out
9	today	6	aunt
11	there	8	baker
12	dentist	10	open
		11	tire

SKIPS CHALLENGE

Q. Why can't a bicycle stand up?

A. Because it's t w o t y r e d !

Page 48-49 Crossword Practice 9

ACROSS		DOWN	
1	butterfly	2	toothbrush
4	tongue	3	free
7	ears	5	glue
8	rich	6	wrist
9	west	9	wet
10	hour	11	over
13	seasons	12	once
15	leaves	14	one

SKIPS CHALLENGE

Q. Why can you now eat your SKIPS book?

A. Because it's a p i e c e o f c a k e !!

NOTES

ORDER FORM

TITLE		RRP
SKIPS KS1 CrossWord Puzzles Key Stage 1 English	ISBN 978-0-9567526-5-9	£7.99
SKIPS KS1 CrossMaths Puzzles Key Stage 1 Maths	ISBN 978-0-9567526-4-2	£7.99
SKIPS KS2 CrossWord Puzzles Key Stage 2 English Book 1	ISBN 978-0-9567526-6-6	£7.99
SKIPS KS2 CrossWord Puzzles Key Stage 2 English Book 2	ISBN 978-0-9567526-2-8	£7.99
SKIPS KS2 CrossMaths Puzzles Key Stage 2 Maths Book 1	ISBN 978-0-9567526-7-3	£7.99
SKIPS KS2 CrossMaths Puzzles Key Stage 2 Maths Book 2	ISBN 978-0-9567526-3-5	£7.99
SKIPS 11+ CrossWord Puzzles 11 Plus English	ISBN 978-0-9567526-0-4	£9.99
SKIPS 11+ CrossMaths Puzzles 11 Plus Maths	ISBN 978-0-9567526-1-1	£9.99

Teachers and Tutors

You will be eligible for discounts on purchases of sets of 10 copies or more. Please get in touch for more details.

 sales@skipscrosswords.co.uk

 www.skipscrosswords.co.uk

 SKIPS Crosswords
142 Newton Road, Great Barr
Birmingham B43 6BT
UK

Skips
Skips
Skips
Skips
Skips
Skips
Skips
Skips
Skips
Skips
Skips
Skips
Skips
Skips
Skips
Skips
Skips
Skips
Skips
Skips
Skips
Skips
Skips
Skips

Skips Challenge stickers